Copyright © 2018 Warner Bros. Entertainment Inc.

FANTASTIC BEASTS AND WHERE TO FIND THEM and FANTASTIC BEASTS: THE CRIMES OF GRINDELWALD
characters, names and related indicia are © & ™ Warner Bros. Entertainment Inc.
WB SHIELD: ™ & © WBEI.
WIZARDING WORLD trademark and logo © & ™
Warner Bros. Entertainment Inc.
Publishing Rights © JKR. (s18)

Written by Emily Stead

www.fantasticbeasts.co.uk

Scholastic Children's Books
Euston House, 24 Eversholt Street,
London NW1 1DB, UK
A division of Scholastic Ltd
London ~ New York ~ Toronto ~ Sydney ~ Auckland
Mexico City ~ New Delhi ~ Hong Kong
First published in the US by Scholastic Inc, 2018
Published in the UK by Scholastic Ltd, 2018

HARDBACK EDITION ISBN 978 1407 18905 5
SCHOLASTIC CLUBS AND FAIRS EDITION ISBN 978 1407 19162 1

Printed and bound in Slovakia

2 4 6 8 10 9 7 5 3 1

Papers used by Scholastic Children's Books are made from wood grown in sustainable forests.

www.scholastic.co.uk

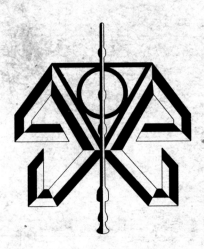

FANTASTIC BEASTS
THE CRIMES OF GRINDELWALD™

MAGICAL MOVIE HANDBOOK

Scholastic Ltd.

CONTENTS

INTRODUCTION...8

CHARACTERS...10

FANTASTIC BEASTS.................................50

ORGANIZATIONS......................................70

LOCATIONS..90

WANDS AND SPELLS.........................116

FANTASTIC BEASTS GALLERY...........132

✳ INTRODUCTION ✳

Newt Scamander, the brilliant Magizoologist is back! His book *Fantastic Beasts and Where to Find Them* has just been published, there are more of his beloved beasts to be discovered and Albus Dumbledore has approached Newt to complete a new mission.

The year is 1927 and Newt is back in London. Only months earlier, Newt and his friends helped to reveal and capture the infamous wizard Gellert Grindelwald, as a Dark energy in the form of an Obscurus tore through New York City. Grindelwald was imprisoned and the Obscurus was thought to have been destroyed by MACUSA (Magical Congress of the United States of America).

However, just as he forewarned, Grindelwald has made a daring escape, and soon discovers that the Obscurus survived the attack in City Hall subway. Support for the Dark wizard's cause is growing – many followers agree that it is time for witches and wizards to rise out of the shadows and rule over all non-magical beings.

Dumbledore calls upon his former student Newt, to find the Obscurus before the Dark wizard can use it as a weapon, this time sending his friend to Paris. Loyalties are tested and lines are drawn in a wizarding world that is more dangerous and divided than ever before.

CHARACTERS

❋ NEWT SCAMANDER ❋

Newt Scamander is a Magizoologist. His aim is to educate the wizarding community about how to live in harmony with magical beasts, ensuring the creatures are protected for generations to come. Newt has completed a world tour, studying magical creatures across the globe, and published a book about his research on his return, entitled *Fantastic Beasts and Where to Find Them* which has become a bestseller.

FULL NAME   Newton Artemis Fido Scamander

DATE OF BIRTH 24th February, 1897

OCCUPATION   Magizoologist, author of *Fantastic Beasts and Where to Find Them*

EDUCATION   Hogwarts School of Witchcraft and Wizardry

HOUSE   Hufflepuff

FAMILY   Theseus Scamander (older brother)

ALLIES   Jacob Kowalski, Tina Goldstein, Queenie Goldstein,
Albus Dumbledore

NEW YORK ADVENTURE

What was supposed to be a brief stopover in New York City in 1926 turned into the greatest adventure of Newt's life. A switch of cases saw him make friends with a No-Maj (non-magical person) and lose his magical creatures in the city, before being arrested, escaping and finally helping to bring down the infamous Dark wizard, Gellert Grindelwald.

A MAGICAL MENAGERIE

Newt has built a secret menagerie in the basement of his London home. It is here that he keeps a whole herd of magical creatures in habitats built especially for them. Everything from an aquatic Kelpie to a family of Nifflers live here, under Newt's care and protection.

A SERIOUS MISSION

Having evaded the Ministry of Magic officials trailing them, Newt and Dumbledore meet on the roof of St Paul's Cathedral in London. Dumbledore asks for Newt's help – he must travel to Paris and find Credence, the Obscurial, before the Dark wizard Grindelwald can use Credence's powers as a deadly weapon. Newt refuses, but once he discovers that his close friend Tina is in the French capital also searching for the Obscurial, he decides to make the journey to find her.

AN ENCHANTED CROSSING

As the Ministry of Magic has rejected Newt's application for a permit to travel, the Magizoologist must travel to France without their knowledge. Newt travels to Paris using a Portkey – an enchanted object that magically transports the user to his or her destination. The Portkey that carries Newt and Jacob to the French capital is an old metal bucket!

✳ GELLERT GRINDLEWALD ✳

Gellert Grindelwald is a formidable wizard who has wreaked havoc across the wizarding world, launching a series of brutal attacks while winning an army of supporters. He has risked exposing the magical community to non-magical people and is wanted by the wizarding authorities worldwide for his crimes.

FULL NAME	Gellert Grindelwald
EDUCATION	Durmstrang Institute
ALLIES	Vinda Rosier, Krall, Nagel, Carrow, MacDuff

DARK DISGUISE

Grindelwald infiltrated MACUSA in New York, Transfiguring into President Picquery's right-hand man, Percival Graves. Newt eventually unmasked the Dark wizard following a duel in New York's City Hall subway. The same battle seemingly saw the Obscurus – a powerful Dark energy – destroyed.

MIDNIGHT ESCAPE

Just as Grindelwald predicted, MACUSA couldn't keep him imprisoned for long. Grindelwald makes a dramatic escape from the rooftop of the Congress's headquarters in a carriage pulled by Thestrals.

FOR THE GREATER GOOD

Grindelwald is intent on overthrowing the International Statute of Secrecy, rules that bind wizards to hide their magic from the non-magical community for their own safety.

WIZARDING WEAPON

Upon discovering that the Obscurial, Credence, has travelled to Paris, Grindelwald pursues him to the French capital.

✳ TINA GOLDSTEIN ✳

Tina Goldstein is an impressive witch. Tina's tenacity saw her narrowly escape death and help bring down Grindelwald in the City Hall subway battle, leading to her being reinstated as a MACUSA Auror. These elite witches and wizards are charged with investigating crimes related to Dark magic.

FULL NAME	Porpentina (Tina) Goldstein
DATE OF BIRTH	19th August, 1901
OCCUPATION	MACUSA Auror, formerly Wand Permit Officer
EDUCATION	Ilvermorny School of Witchcraft and Wizardry
HOUSE	Thunderbird
FAMILY	Queenie Goldstein (sister), parents deceased
ALLIES	Queenie Goldstein, Newt Scamander, Seraphina Picquery

TINA AND NEWT

Tina and Newt grew close during their time spent together in New York and parted on good terms when Newt sailed back home to England. Newt promised to return with a copy of his book, *Fantastic Beasts and Where to Find Them* upon its publication, a promise that, so far, he has been unable to keep.

TINA IN PARIS

Tina travels to Paris, determined to find Credence who she knows is in grave danger.

QUARREL WITH QUEENIE

Tina disapproves of her younger sister's relationship with No-Maj Jacob Kowalski. As a prominent MACUSA employee, Tina's job is to enforce magical law.

TINA TRICKED

While in Paris, Tina meets the mysterious French-African wizard Yusuf Kama, who is also searching for Credence.

✳ QUEENIE GOLDSTEIN ✳

The younger of the Goldstein sisters, Queenie does a lowly desk job in the basement of MACUSA headquarters. The role belies her talents – Queenie is a skilled Legilimens, seamstress and cook. In *Fantastic Beasts and Where to Find Them*, she also masterminded the escape of Newt, Tina and Jacob from the MACUSA building, carrying them to safety in Newt's magical case.

FULL NAME	Queenie Goldstein
OCCUPATION	Desk job at the Wand Permit Office, MACUSA
EDUCATION	Ilvermorny School of Witchcraft and Wizardry
FAMILY	Tina Goldstein (sister), parents deceased
ALLIES	Tina Goldstein, Jacob Kowalski, Newt Scamander

WHIRLWIND ROMANCE

Queenie's life changed forever when she met Jacob. She would like nothing more than to become Mrs Kowalski, but under the strict wizarding world laws in the United States, she is forbidden from marrying her No-Maj sweetheart.

SHOW OF SUPPORT

Intent on finding a way for her and Jacob to be together, Queenie has used magic to whisk Jacob, unwittingly, to England, where magical laws are more progressive. However, the ruse backfires, threatening the budding romance and leaving Queenie desperate … and vulnerable.

✳ JACOB KOWALSKI ✳

No-Maj Jacob Kowalski has been bitten by a Murtlap, charged down by an Erumpent and even Obliviated, yet he remains bewitched by the wizarding world. At the end of *Fantastic Beasts and Where to Find Them*, having lost all memories of his magical adventures with Newt, Queenie and Tina, Jacob was finally able to open his dream bakery thanks to a stranger's gift of pure-silver Occamy eggshells.

FULL NAME	Jacob Kowalski
OCCUPATION	Owner of Kowalski Quality Baked Goods
ALLIES	Newt Scamander, Queenie Goldstein

ENCHANTED

When Jacob and Queenie first met, it was love at first sight. Queenie is attracted to Jacob's honesty – which, thanks to her mind-reading skills, cannot be feigned – while Jacob sees beyond Queenie's obvious beauty to her spark, compassion and warmth. While the pair undoubtedly make a magical match, Jacob was Obliviated and recalls nothing about their time spent together.

SURPRISE VISIT

Jacob and Queenie arrive unexpectedly at Newt's London flat. Newt hasn't seen his friends since leaving New York.

WILLING ASSISTANT

With his memories of the wizarding world returned, Jacob is more than willing to help Newt with his magical creatures. Jacob is fascinated by Newt's beasts – even though he knows exactly how dangerous some species can be first-hand! When Newt decides to head to Paris to find Tina, Jacob agrees to accompany him, hoping to reunite with Queenie.

AMERICAN DREAM

As we learn in the first film, this is not Jacob's first trip to Europe – he fought in the Great War for the American Expeditionary Force and stayed in Europe for six years after the war had ended. Jacob then returned to New York in the hope of realizing his own American Dream – to open a bakery selling Polish pastries.

✳ ALBUS DUMBLEDORE ✳

Acknowledged as one of the most formidable wizards in the world, Albus Dumbledore is a professor of Defence Against the Dark Arts at Hogwarts School of Witchcraft and Wizardry. He and Grindelwald were close as young men, until Dumbledore discovered the full extent of Grindelwald's evil intentions.

FULL NAME	Albus Percival Wulfric Brian Dumbledore
OCCUPATION	Defence Against the Dark Arts teacher, Hogwarts
EDUCATION	Hogwarts School of Witchcraft and Wizardry
HOUSE	Gryffindor
FAMILY	Parents deceased, brother Aberforth, sister Ariana deceased
ALLIES	Newt Scamander

Dumbledore taught Newt Defence Against the Dark Arts at Hogwarts. In one of his lessons, Dumbledore had the students face off against a Boggart.

ROOFTOP REQUEST

Dumbledore and Newt have known each other since Newt was a Hogwarts student and Dumbledore his teacher. Dumbledore arranges a secret meeting on the roof of St Paul's Cathedral to brief Newt on an important task that he is unable to complete himself.

AURORS' STANDOFF

When a convoy of Aurors arrives at Hogwarts uninvited, Dumbledore remains tight-lipped. The Ministry believes that Newt is in Paris on the professor's instructions, while Dumbledore claims that Newt has never been a great follower of orders.

CREDENCE

Credence was raised by his adoptive mother, Mary Lou Barebone, in New York. He was terribly treated by Mary Lou, who told him his real mother was a "wicked and unnatural woman". Credence suffers the terrible burden of being an Obscurial – his body plays host to a Dark and uncontrollable energy that grows inside him like a parasite.

FULL NAME   Credence Barebone, birth name unknown

EDUCATION   Schooled by the New Salem Philanthropic Society

FAMILY   Adoptive mother: Mary Lou Barebone, adoptive sisters:
                        Chastity and Modesty Barebone

ALLIES   The Maledictus

SHOCKING SURVIVAL

Against all odds, Credence survived a powerful magical attack at the wands of MACUSA officials, while in the form of the Obscurus. Nobody witnessed that a tiny wisp of black smoke survived the attack

CREDENCE'S QUEST

Credence begins a quest to find out more about his real family and makes his way to Europe with a travelling circus.

LIFE IN DANGER

Credence is considered a threat to the wizarding world. Grindelwald wants to reunite with him and use his deadly force as an Obscurus for his own means.

A FRIENDSHIP FORMED

Credence meets the Maledictus at Circus Arcanus. Both have known great suffering in their lives and the pair quickly form a bond. The Maledictus encourages Credence to embrace his magic instead of concealing it and Credence begins to control the darkness inside him.

❋ THE MALEDICTUS ❋

The Maledictus is the star attraction at Circus Arcanus. At each show, the Maledictus, who is a beautiful young woman, completes a spectacular transformation into a creature, though a blood curse dictates that one day she is destined to remain permanently in her beast form.

UNDERBEINGS

The Ringmaster Skender describes his acts at Circus Arcanus as 'Underbeings', creatures that are less than human, despite their magical ancestry. He has no respect for them and treats them badly.

LOST SOULS

The Maledictus and Credence find true friendship in one another. She encourages Credence to no longer suppress the magic inside him and learn how to control it. Credence lifts the sorrow from the Maledictus, offering her comfort and respect.

✺ THESEUS SCAMANDER ✺

Theseus is Newt's elder brother. He has a high-profile role as the Head of the British Ministry of Magic's Auror Office, and is a celebrated war hero having fought in the Great War.

FULL NAME	Theseus Scamander
OCCUPATION	Head of the Auror Office, British Ministry of Magic
EDUCATION	Hogwarts School of Witchcraft and Wizardry
FAMILY	Newt Scamander (younger brother)
ALLIES	Leta Lestrange, the British Ministry of Magic

CLOSE COLLEAGUES

Although Newt and Leta were close at school, it is the elder Scamander brother who is now engaged to be married to Leta Lestrange. Theseus and Leta are both employed in the Department of Magical Law Enforcement within the Ministry of Magic.

LETA LESTRANGE

Little is known about Leta Lestrange, a loner whose days at Hogwarts were lifted by her only friend, Newt. Although Leta was raised in England, she belongs to an ancient wizarding family whose roots can be traced back to France.

FULL NAME	Leta Lestrange
OCCUPATION	Works in the Department of Magical Law Enforcement, Ministry of Magic
EDUCATION	Hogwarts School of Witchcraft and Wizardry
HOUSE	Slytherin
ALLIES	Theseus Scamander

RETURN TO HOGWARTS

When Leta returns to Hogwarts on Ministry business, she is reminded of her sorrowful school days. It was at the wizarding school that she and Newt formed a close friendship as they both felt like outsiders. The pair lost touch after Newt left Hogwarts.

FAUX AMIS

In the wizarding world, appearances are rarely what they seem. Newt must face new foes in Paris – wizards and witches who fool those around them and manipulate others to get their own way.

YUSUF KAMA

Yusuf Kama is an elegant French-African wizard, searching for Credence.

SKENDER

Skender offers a home at Circus Arcanus to 'Underbeings'. His benevolence comes at a cost to any human or creature that joins the circus, though, as Skender treats them poorly.

BUNTY

Bunty is Newt's assistant. She cares for the magical creatures in Newt's menagerie basement while he travels abroad. Bunty adores the beasts almost as much as Newt does – even though they like to nip – and has a soft spot for the Magizoologist too.

✳ NICOLAS FLAMEL ✳

Known to be over 600 years old, the accomplished alchemist Nicolas Flamel is the only known maker of the legendary Philosopher's Stone, which has thus far granted him immortality. An ally of Dumbledore's for many years, Flamel aids Newt on his mission.

NICOLAS FLAMEL
51 Rue de Montmorency
Paris

The Philosopher's Stone produces the Elixir of Life and can transform any metal into gold.

❋ FANTASTIC BEASTS ❋

BOWTRUCKLE

The sprig-like Bowtruckle is a maximum of eight inches in height and appears to be made out of a tree stem with roots, tiny leafy branches and two brown eyes. Normally gentle creatures, unless threatened, and then they will do whatever it takes to defend their home. Bowtruckles only nest in trees that produce wand-quality wood.

Intensely shy creatures, Bowtruckles become calm whenever Newt is nearby.

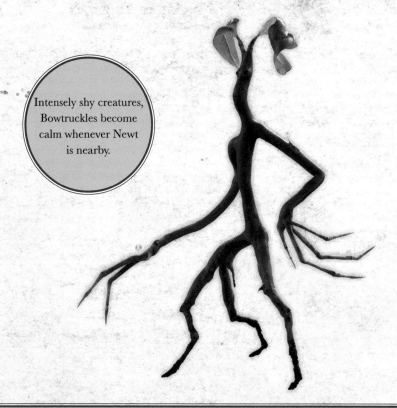

SPECIAL ABILITIES:

※ Bowtruckles are excellent hiders and blend in with their natural habitat, making them difficult to spot

※ Their long, sharp twig-like fingers prove handy for picking locks

PICKETT

Pickett is Newt's ever-present travel companion, and prefers to spend his time in the top pocket of Newt's coat.

※ In the film *Fantastic Beasts and Where to Find Them*, Pickett saved the lives of Newt and Tina when he unpicked the lock to Newt's handcuffs while the pair was imprisoned in a MACUSA cell.

※ Newt once agreed to trade his tiny twig-creature with Gnarlak in exchange for information – Pickett was not amused!

NIFFLER

Don't be deceived by these gentle and even affectionate beasts; owning a Niffler as a pet may come at a cost. With dark fur, beady eyes and a bill like a platypus, Nifflers are always on the hunt for glittering objects and will steal anything that catches their eye.

It is not recommended that Nifflers are kept as domestic pets.

SPECIAL ABILITIES:

✷ Once a Niffler has sniffed out a shiny treasure, it conceals it in an expanding pouch

✷ Like Bowtruckles, Nifflers have cunning powers of escape

❋ Newt has a family of Nifflers with four babies in his company. These Nifflers get up to all sorts of mischief in their search for shiny objects. Nothing comes between Nifflers and their treasure!

❋ Newt decides to let the Nifflers travel in his case as he and Jacob search for Tina in Paris. Might their magical tracking powers prove a useful asset?

THESTRAL

Thestrals are visible only to those who have witnessed death first-hand. Then, they appear as skeletal but strong winged beasts with long, bat-like wings, forked hooves and a pointed tail.

Grindelwald makes his escape from the rooftop of MACUSA headquarters in a carriage pulled by Thestrals.

SPECIAL ABILITY:

 Invisibility, to those fortunate enough not to have witnessed death

☀ The core of Grindelwald's Elder Wand is rumoured to be Thestral tail hair.

☀ Despite their spooky appearance, Thestrals are misunderstood creatures. They are in fact gentle beasts that can be tamed.

KELPIE

This creature lives underwater, where its camouflage is looking like long, thick strands of green kelp.

SPECIAL ABILITIES:

✳ The Kelpie is extremely strong and hard to tame with a nasty bite

✳ Once bridled, the Kelpie is docile and, for those who know how to handle it, the Kelpie can provide a fast underwater ride

Newt cares for an injured Kelpie in a pool in his basement.

AUGUREY

The Augurey is a large, owl-like bird with sharp talons and a horned beak. On its head, the Augurey has long, individual tendrils that feather out at the ends. Its long tail feathers are dark green and interspersed with pretty purple and green plumes.

MATAGOT

The feline Matagot is a spirit familiar somewhat resembling a hairless Sphinx cat.

SPECIAL ABILITIES:

✳ In France, they are utilized by Le Ministère des Affaires Magiques to do menial jobs, including providing security for various departments

✳ Matagots won't attack unless provoked, but then they will transform into something far more menacing

A Chupacabra is part-lizard, part-humanoid. This creature from the Americas has markings that are blue with red rings. It is a vicious blood-sucking creature.

FIREDRAKE

The Firedrake looks like a small flying lizard with long antennae.

SPECIAL ABILITY:

 The Firedrake emits sparks from the end of its tail that set anything flammable ablaze

ZOUWU

The Zouwu is a monstrously large feline beast – as big as an elephant – with a striped body, scraggly mane, four fangs that curl up out of its mouth and long, sharp claws. It has a distinctive multi-coloured tail.

SPECIAL ABILITY:

✷ Zouwu's are incredibly powerful and fast, capable of travelling 1000 miles in a day

An Obscurus is an uncontrollable Dark energy that relies on a host to keep it alive. The Obscurus in New York appeared as a ferocious dark shadow with eyes. Its explosive outbursts devastated the city. An Obscurus inhabits the body of a young child in which it grows like a parasite.

✳ The Obscurus consumes so much energy that its host – the Obscurial – typically does not live longer than a decade.

✳ Newt trapped an Obscurus in Sudan, Africa, in a shimmering box for further study. Newt insists that his Obscurus is harmless as the young girl who was its host died.

✳ At the end of *Fantastic Beasts and Where to Find Them*, MACUSA believed that the Obscurus within Credence was destroyed, though the tiniest wisp of a black shadow survived.

✸ ORGANIZATIONS ✸

Each country in the wizarding world has its own ministry that governs its magical community. The ministries make laws to protect the community, keeping all magical affairs secret from non-magical people. Exposing the wizarding world would lead to conflict and untold danger.

The Ministry of Magic (M.o.M.) for Great Britain is based in the centre of London.

AURORS

Aurors are the Ministry's elite witches and wizards that are trained to investigate crimes related to Dark magic. They belong to the Department of Magical Law Enforcement. Theseus Scamander is Head of the Auror Office, while the Ministry wants to recruit Newt to the department, too, to help capture Credence.

MINISTRY MISSION

As Newt will not help the Ministry find Credence, he is refused a permit to travel. Newt wishes to have no part in any mission that would cause Credence harm.

BEING WATCHED

The Ministry keeps detailed files on Albus Dumbledore, tracking his every move. Old friends Newt and Dumbledore must use magic to outwit those trailing them before meeting on the rooftop of St Paul's Cathedral in London.

TRAVEL PLANS

Dumbledore says he cannot take on Grindelwald himself. Instead, he asks his former Hogwarts pupil Newt to help, but Newt refuses.

The Magical Congress of the United States of America (or MACUSA) is the organization that governs the country's magical community from its New York headquarters. MACUSA orders every witch and wizard to carry a wand permit, in order to keep tabs on any magical activity performed on its shores.

PRESIDENT PICQUERY

Commanding MACUSA President Seraphina Picquery believes in keeping the magical community hidden from No-Majs at all costs. It was on her orders that the Obscurus was believed to have been destroyed.

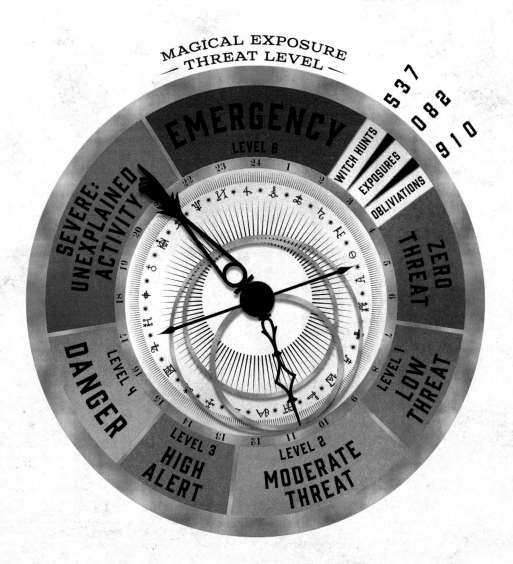

MAGICAL EXPOSURE
THREAT LEVEL

EMERGENCY
LEVEL 8

SEVERE: UNEXPLAINED ACTIVITY

WITCH HUNTS

EXPOSURES

OBLIVIATIONS

ZERO THREAT

DANGER

LEVEL 4

LEVEL 1
LOW THREAT

LEVEL 3
HIGH ALERT

LEVEL 2
MODERATE THREAT

537
082
910

MAGICAL MONITOR

The Magical Exposure Threat Level Clock hangs in the lobby of MACUSA
headquarters. It monitors how critical the threat level is to the wizarding community.
In *Fantastic Beasts and Where to Find Them*, when Newt and Tina entered the building
together, the dial swung to show 'SEVERE: UNEXPLAINED ACTIVITY'.

✳ GRINDELWALD'S FLIGHT ✳

Just as Grindelwald promised in the subway battle in New York, MACUSA could not hold him for long. The Dark wizard makes a rooftop escape as he is being transferred from the Congress's headquarters to stand trial for his crimes in Europe.

FOR THE GREATER GOOD

Grindelwald believes wizards should have dominion over all non-magical people.

Grindelwald's carriage is pulled by ghostly Thestrals.

LE MINISTÈRE DES AFFAIRES MAGIQUES DE LA FRANCE

The French Ministry of Magic is based in the centre of Paris. It is a beautiful building with decorative Art Nouveau features, including a glass dome decorated with magical creatures.

UNUSUAL ENTRANCE

Ministry officials access the building by entering a birdcage-shaped lift, which reveals itself from the roots of a tree.

WIZARDING REGISTER

The names of all French witches and wizards are listed in a register of magical families.

✷ CIRCUS ARCANUS ✷

Circus Arcanus is a travelling circus that promises a colourful and spectacular show of living curiosities. Behind the glamour of the big top, though, the circus is a miserable place. Many beasts were captured from the wild and traded, before being forced to perform at the circus.

LE CIRQUE
ARCANUS

**MUSÉE
DES
CURIOSITÉS
VIVANTES**

TERRIBLE TREATMENT

The owner and Ringmaster of Circus Arcanus, Skender, offers shelter to 'freaks and oddities', but at a terrible price. Many 'Underbeings' and rare magical creatures are kept in cages. It is at the circus that Credence and the Maledictus first meet.

The Kappa, a Japanese water demon, is one of the Circus's main attractions.

GRINDELWALD'S ACOLYTES

Even though Grindelwald was imprisoned, support for the Dark wizard grew during the time he spent behind bars. Now at large, Grindelwald and his manifesto offer hope to witches and wizards who have been forced to conceal their magic before the non-magical community.

Nagel, Krall, Carrow and Rosier are part of Grindelwald's inner circle.

NAGEL

KRALL

CARROW

ROSIER

VINDA ROSIER

Vinda Rosier is willing to carry out any task her master demands.

Grindelwald trusts Rosier as one of his most loyal supporters.

✳ LOCATIONS ✳

❋ NEW YORK CITY ❋

In *Fantastic Beasts and Where to Find Them*, the Goldstein sisters have some grand adventures in the Big Apple, not least when a certain Magizoologist came to town and stayed at their apartment with his No-Maj friend. On their next adventure, both Tina and Queenie travel to Europe for different reasons – Tina to find Credence and Queenie in the hope that the laws across the pond will allow her to be with Jacob.

MACUSA HEADQUARTERS

America's wizarding ministry monitors and protects wizardkind. Its looming headquarters are in downtown New York City. Both Goldstein sisters are employed there and Grindelwald infiltrated the organization in the guise of Percival Graves.

FOND FAREWELL

Newt and Tina shared a tender goodbye at the docks in New York, before Newt returned to England by ship. He promised to return to deliver a copy of his book in person when it was published, which delighted Tina.

✳ LONDON LANDMARKS ✳

Dumbledore and Newt must meet in secret to discuss the mission that Dumbledore has set for Newt. The wizards meet at one of London's most famous landmarks, away from the Ministry's spies.

TRUSTED FRIENDS

Newt and Dumbledore meet on the rooftop of St Paul's Cathedral in the City of London. Dumbledore is more than a schoolteacher to Newt and the friends trust and respect each other completely.

✳ NEWT'S MENAGERIE ✳

As the world's leading Magizoologist, Newt has created a huge menagerie in the basement of his London home with a collection of natural habitats created especially for the magical creatures in Newt's care.

CURIOUS KELPIES

A deep pool is home to an injured Kelpie, its camouflage helps it blend in with its underwater surroundings, as it looks like strands of kelp. Magizoologist, Newt, knows how to handle this powerful beast as it takes him for a wild underwater ride.

ANIMAL AILMENTS

Newt's collection of potions will cure any injured or poorly animal. He often recovers hurt magical creatures to his menagerie from his travels, nursing them back to health before returning them to the wild.

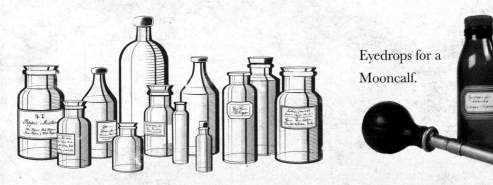

Eyedrops for a Mooncalf.

MINISTRATION CHART

Newt's Ministration Chart lists special feed codes and habitat and terrain codes for each of his creatures, based on their natural habitats. Newt and his assistant, Bunty, care for each beast as though it were in the wild.

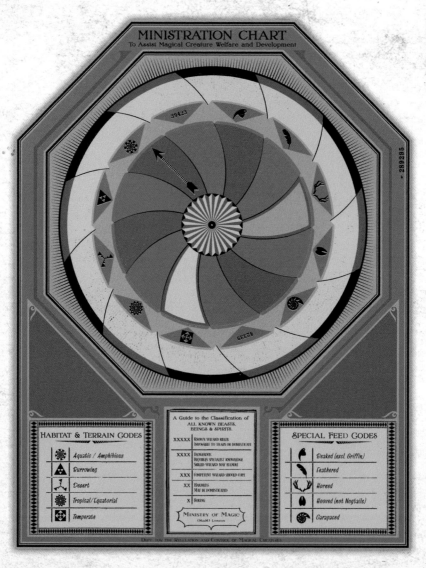

TRAVELLING BEASTS

Newt's magical case is a smaller, portable version of his menagerie. When he travels to Paris, he packs a family of Nifflers safely in his luggage, while Pickett the Bowtruckle accompanies Newt in his top pocket.

ABLE ASSISTANT

Bunty is in charge of the menagerie whenever Newt is away. She is as passionate about the care of magical creatures as the famous Magizoologist himself.

HOGWARTS SCHOOL OF WITCHCRAFT AND WIZARDRY

Hogwarts is a wizarding school in the United Kingdom where children with magical abilities can learn everything from Transfiguration to potion making.

PREVIOUS PUPILS

The four Hogwarts houses are Gryffindor, Hufflepuff, Ravenclaw and Slytherin.
Former pupils of the magical school include Albus Dumbledore, Leta Lestrange and
Newt Scamander. Newt was sorted into Hufflepuff and, despite being expelled from
Hogwarts, packed his old school scarf when he travelled to New York in winter.

UNWANTED VISITORS

An uninvited party of Aurors from the Ministry of Magic arrive at Hogwarts to interview professor Albus Dumbledore.

TORQUIL TRAVERS

The party is led by Torquil Travers, the tough-talking Head of Magical Law Enforcement at the Ministry.

✳ DUMBLEDORE'S CLASSROOM ✳

The Ministry Aurors question Dumbledore about Newt's whereabouts in the professor's classroom. Defence Against the Dark Arts is a core class at Hogwarts, where pupils are taught how to magically defend themselves against Dark magic, including Dark charms and dangerous creatures.

MAGICAL ARTEFACTS

Dumbledore's classroom is full of fascinating magical items.

✳ TWENTIES PARIS ✳

While New York and London enjoyed the Roaring Twenties, the same decade in Paris was known as Les Années Folles (the crazy years). It was a period of rich social, cultural and artistic change in the city. Many buildings were built in the beautiful Art Nouveau architectural style.

TRAVEL BY PORTKEY

Newt and Jacob pitch up in Paris using a Portkey, an enchanted object that magically transports them to their destination. Newt and Jacob's Portkey is an old metal bucket.

CHANNEL CROSSING

Newt and Jacob must first travel to the White Cliffs of Dover on the English coast to begin their crossing.

CAFÉ SOCIETY

As they walk through the streets of Paris, Newt and Jacob encounter the wizard Yusuf Kama outside a café in the city.

✳ ABOVE THE CITY ✳

Having fled Circus Arcanus, Credence and Maledictus must stay out of plain sight. They camp out on the rooftop of a tall stone building, away from the hustle and bustle of city life below.

UNDER CONTROL

As Credence is no longer forced to conceal his magic, he is gaining strength and learning how to control the Obscurus. Credence and the Maledictus find a safe place to stay in a Paris building and explore the rooftop.

✳ KAMA'S HIDEOUT ✳

Yusuf Kama's base in Paris is an underground hideout in the sewers below the famous River Seine. It is here that he carries out his research as part of his quest to find Credence.

FAMILY TREE

Evidence of Kama's fascination with one pureblood family can be seen engraved on the sewer walls.

MYSTERIOUS MOTIVES

Tina and Kama visit a Parisian café – having no reason to mistrust him,
Tina goes with Kama to his hideout.

WANDS AND SPELLS

A wand is an important tool that channels the magical energies of a witch or wizard. A simple-looking wand does not mean that it cannot cast a powerful spell, as the strength of the magic comes from within the caster.

NEWT SCAMANDER

Newt's modest wand is a simple design that reflects that natural world he cares so much about.

TINA GOLDSTEIN

Tina has no requirement for an ornate wand. Her plain wooden wand perfectly reflects this no-nonsense witch.

> Wands can be made from various woods from alder to yew. At the core of each wand is a magical material such as a unicorn hair or phoenix feather.

QUEENIE GOLDSTEIN

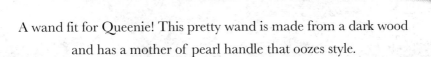

A wand fit for Queenie! This pretty wand is made from a dark wood and has a mother of pearl handle that oozes style.

ALBUS DUMBLEDORE

Dumbledore's wand can cast some of the most powerful magical spells the wizarding world has ever seen.

LETA LESTRANGE

A dark wood wand with a silver and carved-wood
handle belongs to Leta.

THESEUS SCAMANDER

An Auror must be in possession of a powerful wand
such as this example at all times.

NICOLAS FLAMEL

A wand that has survived alongside its wizard for centuries, Flamel's wand has a curved handle made from a dragon's claw.

YUSUF KAMA

A combination of dark and lighter woods, Kama's wand is slim and subtle.

THE ELDER WAND

The ancient Elder Wand is said to be the most powerful wand in the wizarding world. Made of elder wood, it measures fifteen inches long and has a core of Thestral tail-hair. It is believed to have been made by Death himself.

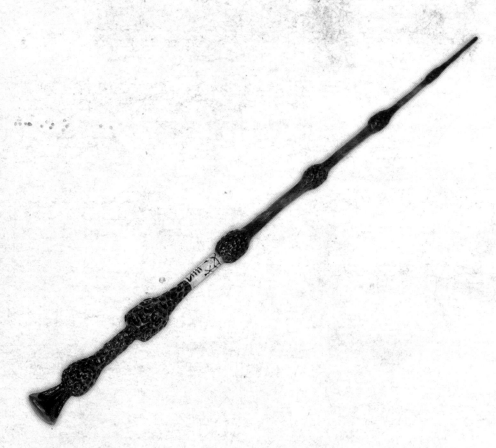

The coveted wand is returned to Grindelwald following his escape from the rooftop of MACUSA headquarters by one of his acolytes.

DEATHLY HALLOWS

The Elder Wand makes up one third of the Deathly Hallows – three magical artefacts that together are said to grant immortality. The Resurrection Stone and Invisibility Cloak make up the legendary trio.

The Deathly Hallows appear at the heart of Grindelwald's symbol.

SPELLS

Witches and wizards are taught to cast simple spells from their very first weeks at wizarding school. Spells can be cast without saying the incantation out loud, though this requires a certain amount of skill, while the most powerful witches and wizards may also produce magic without a wand.

ACCIO

Summons an object

APPARE VESTIGIUM

Shows footprints and track marks

# AVENSEGIUM

Transforms an object into a tracking device

# ALOHOMORA

Opens locked doors, windows or objects

# CONFUNDUS

Causes confusion in person or sentient object

# EXPELLIARMUS

Disarms an opponent's wand

LUMOS

Conjures light

NEBULUS

Conjures fog

OSCAUSI

Seals someone's mouth shut

PROTEGO DIABOLICA

Conjures a protective circle of fire

REPARO

Reassembles or fixes something that has been broken

REVELIO

Reveals intruders and imposters

RIDDIKULUS

Makes a Boggart less threatening

STUPEFY

Used to knock out an opponent in a duel

SURGITO

Removes an enchantment

VENTUS

Traps a person in a hurricane for one

FANTASTIC BEASTS GALLERY

AUGUREY